NHIE STUDY GUIDE

NHIE STUDY GUIDE

Examination Board of Professional Home Inspectors

NHIE STUDY GUIDE

ISBN: 978-0-9964518-1-9

Disclaimer of Liability

REFERENCES

American Heritage Dictionary of the English Language
Fifth Edition

Garner's Modern American Usage 2003
Bryan A. Garner

Professional Home Inspector Role Delineation Study (Abridged)
February 2013
Examination Board of Professional Home Inspectors

TABLE OF CONTENTS

PREFACE

This educational material is meant to assist the student in understanding the general content and format for the National Home Inspector Examination (NHIE). This information is divided into two volumes. This volume is the *NHIE Study Guide*. The other volume is the *NHIE Home Inspection Manual*. This information was compiled with the most recent information, and every effort has been made to provide the most accurate information available. We welcome any suggestions at our website at: www.homeinspectionexam.org.

1: ABOUT THE NATIONAL HOME INSPECTOR EXAMINATION

INTRODUCTION

Home inspection, once an individual activity, has matured over the last forty years into a specific professional discipline with a set of standards, ethics, and accepted procedures. As part of the growth of this profession the majority of states require some type of home inspector licensing. The National Home Inspector Examination (NHIE) plays a vital role in establishing the baseline for minimum knowledge to enter the profession. This study guide is to help prepare candidates to take the NHIE.

While technical knowledge is an important aspect of being a home inspector, attention to detail and good verbal and written communication skills are vital in providing the home inspection service. This study guide makes no attempt to define or to develop these skills, but the candidate is advised to focus on development of these important skills in order to properly serve the client.

This series, designed to help candidates prepare for the NHIE, consists of two volumes. This volume, the *NHIE Study Guide* (Study Guide), includes general examination and study information, and information on adminstrative procedures. The second volume, the *NHIE Home Inspection Manual* (Manual), includes specific technical content of primary importance to the current examination being offered.

The reader of this material is expected to have some basic knowledge of building components and terms, and the technical material is written with this expectation in mind. A detailed glossary is provided in each section of the Manual. An index is also provided in order to assist with quickly locating specific topics.

There are also two hundred sample examination questions provided. One hundred of these questions are in the Manual and the other one hundred are in this Study Guide. (The NHIE consists of one hundred questions.) These questions have been developed and reviewed in the same way as the active questions in the NHIE test bank, and are presented in the appropriate technical content areas.

DEVELOPMENT OF THIS STUDY GUIDE

A common question The Examination Board of Professional Home Inspectors (EBPHI) has received over the years is: "What should I study?" EBPHI has always provided a list of reference books used in the development of examination questions, but requiring a candidate to purchase and digest information in all reference books is often not realistic or prudent. This series, consisting of the Manual and the Study Guide, are the result of several years of research and development. The goal is to provide the home inspection candidate with basic knowledge in a logical format.

The examination content outline is produced from and directly reflects the latest Role Delineation Study (RDS) performed in 2011. This national study is performed approximately every five years. It defines the home inspection profession by bringing together working home inspectors from different regions of the United States and Canada. Many of these home inspectors are affiliated with home inspector professional organizations such as The American Society of Home Inspectors (ASHI), International Association of Certified Home Inspectors (InterNachi), The National Association of Home Inspectors (NAHI), and various State professional organizations. The group of home inspectors also includes those who are non-affiliated. These home inspectors define the various content areas and the number of examination questions within each area. This is essentially how the NHIE reflects what home inspectors are actually doing in the field, thereby assessing professional competency.

ABOUT THE EXAMINATION BOARD OF PROFESSIONAL HOME INSPECTORS (EBPHI)

The Examination Board of Professional Home Inspectors (EBPHI) is an independent, not-for-profit corporation founded in 1999. The mission of EBPHI is: "to establish the standard of competence for home inspectors and to enhance consumer confidence in home inspection professionals." The EBPHI addresses this mission by encouraging regulatory bodies in state and local governments, as well as professional membership organizations, to adopt the NHIE for competency assessment.

HOME INSPECTION REGULATION

Administration of the NHIE ensures that home inspection professionals meet basic knowledge and practice requirements for purposes of regulation. Successful completion of the examination answers the needs of the public, the various governmental bodies, and of home inspectors. The examination is administered nationwide by several vendors. For information about home inspection laws and regulations, see EBPHI's website at www.homeinspectionexam.org.

THE NATIONAL HOME INSPECTION EXAMINATION (NHIE)

The NHIE is based on a formal Role Delineation Study (RDS) that defines the profession as practiced in the field. Home inspection subject matter experts from a variety of practice specialties and geographic areas contribute to the study, and home inspectors from throughout the nation then review the study via a statistically valid survey. The resulting content areas and their associated knowledge and skill requirements serve as the basis for the NHIE. This examination development methodology is in accordance with accepted psychometric standards for a high stakes public protection examination. These standards are promulgated by organizations such as the American Education Research Association (AERA), the National Council for Certifying Agencies (NCCA), the American Psychological Association (APA) and the Equal Employment Opportunity Commission (EEOC).

ONLINE PRACTICE EXAMINATION

Candidates can now take the practice examination online at www.homeinspectionexam.org to prepare for the NHIE. Please note that the practice examination is intended to help candidates become familiar with the general types of questions that may appear on a licensing examination. It is not a substitute for education and study. Furthermore, scoring well on the practice examination does not guarantee a positive outcome on the actual NHIE. Note: Candidates may take the practice examination an unlimited number of times; however, payment will be required each time. The practice examination fee is $50.

2: THE NATIONAL HOME INSPECTOR EXAMINATION CONTENT OUTLINE

The following content outline is derived from the most recent Role Delineation Study (RDS) and is intended to inform candidates about topics that may appear as questions on the National Home Inspector Examination (NHIE). The percentage of questions on the NHIE for each domain and task is indicated below. This outline is not a complete listing of all topics covered by the NHIE, and does not represent all skills necessary to perform a competent home inspection.

PERFORMANCE DOMAIN I: BUILDING SCIENCE (64%)

Task 1 - Site Conditions

Identify and inspect site conditions, using applicable standards for material selection and installation procedures, to assess immediate and long term safety and maintenance issues that may affect people or the performance of the building. (5%)

a. Vegetation, Grading, Drainage, and Retaining Walls

  i.   Common retaining wall types, materials, applications, installation methods, construction techniques, and clearance requirements
  ii.   Common grading and drainage system types, materials, applications, installation methods, and construction techniques
  iii. Typical defects (e.g., negative grade, site drainage problems)
  iv.   Typical vegetation and landscape conditions, maintenance practices, and how they affect the building
  v.   Maintenance concerns and procedures
  vi.   Safety issues, applicable standards, and appropriate terminology

b. Driveways, Patios, and Walkways

  i.   Common types, materials, applications, installation methods, and construction techniques
  ii.   Typical defects (e.g. root damage, trip hazards)
  iii. Maintenance concerns and procedures
  iv.   Safety issues, applicable standards, and appropriate terminology

c. Decks, Balconies, Stoops, Stairs, Steps, Porches, and Applicable Railings

  i.   Common types, materials, applications, installation methods, and construction techniques
  ii.   Attachment methods (e.g., lag screws, bolts, ledgers, cantilevered flooring)
  iii. Deck load transfer to supporting soil theory (e.g., deck to joist, to girder, to post, to soil)
  iv.   Typical defects (e.g., flashing, railings, decayed wood, results of deferred maintenance)
  v.   Maintenance/design concerns and procedures
  vi.   Safety issues, applicable standards, and appropriate terminology

Task 2 - Exterior Components

Identify and inspect building exterior components, using applicable standards for material selection and installation procedures, to assess immediate and long term safety and maintenance issues that may affect people or the performance of the building. (6%)

a. Wall Cladding, Flashing, Trim, Eaves, Soffits, and Fascia

i.   Common types (e.g., stucco, composite siding, brick veneer, vinyl siding, EIFS, step flashing)
ii. Typical defects (e.g., cracking, improper installation, water infiltration, decay)
iii. Maintenance concerns and procedures
iv. Safety issues, applicable standards, and appropriate terminology

b. Exterior Doors and Windows

i.   Common door and window types, materials, applications, installation methods, and construction techniques
ii. Typical defects (e.g., delaminating, decayed wood, hermetic seal failure, flashing, cracked glass)
iii. Maintenance concerns and procedures
iv. Safety issues, applicable standards, appropriate terminology, and glazing requirements (e.g., egress requirements, safety glazing, release for security bars)

c. Roof Coverings

i.   Common roof covering types, materials, applications, installation methods, construction techniques, and manufacturer's requirements
ii. Typical roof covering repair methods and materials
iii. Typical defects (e.g., improper installation, cracking, curling, deterioration, damage)
iv. Characteristics of different roof covering materials
v.   Sheathing and underlayment requirements for different types of roof coverings
vi. Maintenance concerns and procedures
vii. Safety issues, applicable standards, and appropriate terminology

d. Roof Drainage Systems

i.   Common roof drainage system types, materials, applications, installation methods, and construction techniques (e.g., roof slope, gutters, roof drains, scuppers)
ii. Typical modifications, repairs, upgrades, and retrofit methods and materials
iii. Typical defects (e.g., ponding, improper slope, clogging/leaking, disposal of roof water runoff)
iv. Maintenance concerns and procedures
v.   Safety issues, applicable standards, and appropriate terminology

e. Flashing

i.   Common types, materials, applications, installation methods, and construction techniques
ii. Typical defects (e.g., separation, corrosion, improper installation, missing flashing)
iii. Maintenance concerns and procedures
iv. Safety issues, applicable standards, and appropriate terminology

f. Skylights and Other Roof Penetrations

i. Common skylight and other roof penetration types, materials, applications, installation methods, and construction techniques

ii. Typical defects (e.g., cracked glazing, improper installation, deterioration, failure, faulty flashing)

iii. Maintenance concerns and procedures

iv. Safety issues, applicable standards, and appropriate terminology

Task 3 - Structural Components

Identify and inspect structural system components, using applicable standards for material selection and installation procedures, to assess immediate and long term safety and maintenance issues that may affect people or the structural stability of the building. (7%)

a. Foundation

i. Common foundation types, materials, applications, installation methods, and construction techniques

ii. Typical foundation modifications, repairs, upgrades, and retrofit methods and materials

iii. Typical defects (e.g., cracks, settlement, decomposition, failed dampproofing) and their common causes and effects

iv. Soil types and conditions and how they affect foundations

v. Applied forces and how they affect foundations (e.g., wind and seismic forces)

vi. Safety issues, applicable standards, and appropriate terminology

vii. Water management (e.g., grading, foundation drains, sump pumps)

b. Floor Structure

i. Common floor system types (e.g., trusses, concrete slabs), materials, applications, installation methods, and construction techniques

ii. Typical modifications, repairs, upgrades, and retrofits methods and materials

iii. Typical defects (e.g., improper cuts and notches in structural members, decayed or damaged structural members, effects of long-term loading and/or bearing and environmental exposure)

iv. Limitations of framing materials (e.g., span)

v. Applied forces and how they affect floor systems (e.g., wind and seismic forces)

vi. Safety issues, applicable standards, and appropriate terminology

c. Walls and Vertical Support Structures

i. Common types, materials, applications, installation methods, and construction techniques

ii. Typical modifications, repairs, upgrades, and retrofit methods and materials

iii. Typical defects (e.g., decayed or damaged structural members, earth to wood contact, structural deformation)

iv. Seismic and wind-resistant construction methods and hardware

v. Fireblocking and firewalls

vi. Safety issues, applicable standards, and appropriate terminology

d. Roof and Ceiling Structures

i. Common roof and ceiling structure types, materials, applications, installation methods, and construction techniques

ii. Typical roof structure modifications, repairs, upgrades, and retrofit methods and materials

iii. Acceptable truss and ceiling structural member modifications, repairs, upgrades, and retrofit methods and materials
iv. Roof and ceiling structure conditions and defects (e.g., moisture stains, fungal/mold growth, sagging rafters, modified/damaged trusses, decayed or damaged structural members)
v. Limitations of framing materials (e.g., span)
vi. Applied forces and how they affect roof/ceiling structures (e.g., wind and seismic forces)
vii. Safety issues, applicable standards, and appropriate terminology
viii. Seismic and wind-resistant construction and hardware
ix. Maintenance concerns and procedures

Task 4 -The Electrical System

Identify and inspect electrical system components, using applicable standards for material selection and installation procedures, to assess immediate and long term safety and maintenance issues that may affect people or the performance of the building. (7%)

a. Electrical Service: Service Entrance, Service Lateral, Service Conductors, Service Equipment, and Service Grounding

i. Common types, materials, applications, installation methods, and construction techniques
ii. Typical modifications, repairs, upgrades, and retrofit methods and materials
iii. Typical defects (e.g., water and rust in panel, equipment height, deteriorated cable sheathing)
iv. Electrical service capacity
v. Service grounding and bonding
vi. Maintenance concerns and procedures
vii. Safety issues, applicable standards, and appropriate terminology

b. Interior Components of Service Panels and Subpanels

i. Common types, materials, applications, installation methods, and construction techniques
ii. Typical modifications, repairs, upgrades, and retrofit methods and materials
iii. Typical defects (e.g., subpanel not bonded, double tapping, overfused conductors)
iv. Main disconnects
v. Panel grounding and subpanel neutral isolation
vi. Panel wiring
vii. Overcurrent protection devices
viii. Function of circuit breakers and fuses
ix. Maintenance concerns and procedures
x. Inspection safety procedures
xi. Safety issues, applicable standards, and appropriate terminology

c. Wiring Systems

i. Common types, materials, applications, and installation methods
ii. Typical modifications, repairs, upgrades, and retrofit methods and materials
iii. Typical defects (e.g., open splices, exposed nonmetallic cable)
iv. Issues involving solid conductor aluminum wire
v. Obsolete electrical wiring systems (e.g., knob and tube wiring)
vi. Maintenance concerns and procedures
vii. Safety issues, applicable standards, and appropriate terminology

d. Devices, Equipment, and Fixtures (e.g., switches, receptacles, lights)

   i.   Common types, materials, applications, installation methods, and construction techniques

   ii.   Typical modifications, repairs, upgrades, and retrofit methods and materials

   iii. Typical defects (e.g., reverse polarity, open grounds, faulty ground fault circuit interruptors (GFCIs))

   iv. Equipment grounding

   v.   Wiring, operation, location of typical devices and equipment (e.g., receptacles and lights, appliances, GFCI protection, arc fault protection)

   vi. Maintenance concerns and procedures

   vii. Safety issues, applicable standards, and appropriate terminology

Task 5 - The Cooling System

Identify and inspect cooling systems, using applicable standards for material selection and installation procedures, to assess immediate and long term safety and maintenance issues that may affect people or the performance of the building. (5%)

a. Cooling

   i.   Common types, materials, applications, installation methods, and construction techniques

   ii.   Typical defects (e.g., suction line insulation missing, condensation and/or rust on components, not cooling properly, condenser not level, frost/ice formation on components, restriction of air flow at the condenser, location of condenser)

   iii. Theory of refrigerant cycle (latent load and sensible load)

   iv. Theory of heat transfer

   v.   Theory of equipment sizing

   vi. Methods of testing the systems

   vii. Condensate control and disposal

   viii. Maintenance concerns and procedures

   ix. Safety issues, applicable standards, and appropriate terminology

b. Distribution Systems

   i.   Common distribution system types, materials, applications, installation methods, and construction techniques

   ii.   Typical defects (damaged ducts, incorrect duct configuration/installation, insufficient air flow, condensation at supply registers, blower operation, improper air temperature at register)

   iii. Methods of testing the system

   iv. Maintenance concerns and procedures (e.g., filter, condensate pump and lines)

   v.   Safety issues, applicable standards, and appropriate terminology

Task 6 - The Heating System

Identify and inspect heating systems, using applicable standards for material selection and installation procedures, to assess immediate and long term safety and maintenance issues that may affect people or the performance of the building. (6%)

a. Heating

   i.   Common types, materials, applications, installation methods, and construction techniques

   ii.   Typical defects (e.g., cracked heat exchanger, dirty fan, improper fuel line installation/ material)

   iii. Theory of heat transfer and how it takes place in different heating system types

   iv. Heating system types (e.g., forced air, gravity, boiler, hydronic, heat pump, solid-fuel)

v.   Theory of equipment sizing
vi.   Methods of testing the systems
vii.   Performance parameters
viii.   Condensate control and disposal
ix.   Byproducts of combustion (e.g., H_2O, CO_2, CO, NO_x), how they are created, and how and when they become a safety hazard
x.   Maintenance concerns and procedures
xi.   Safety issues, applicable standards, and appropriate terminology

b. Distribution Systems

i.   Common distribution system types, materials, applications, installation methods, and construction techniques
ii.   Typical defects (e.g., damaged ducts, incorrect duct configuration/installation, insufficient airflow, blower operation, and improper air temperature at register)
iii.   Methods of testing the system
iv.   Maintenance concerns and procedures (e.g., filter, humidifier)
v.   Safety issues, applicable standards, and appropriate terminology

c. Flue and Vent Systems

i.   Common vent system types, materials, applications, installation methods, and construction techniques
ii.   Typical defects (e.g., separated vent, backdrafting, clearance to combustible materials, proper slope, combustion air and makeup air duct sizing and configuration)
iii.   Theory of venting and exhaust flues
iv.   Equipment sizing
v.   Safety issues, applicable standards, and appropriate terminology

Task 7 - Insulation and Ventilation

Identify and inspect insulation, moisture management systems, and attic/interior/crawl space ventilation systems in conditioned and unconditioned spaces, using applicable standards for material selection and installation procedures, to assess the immediate condition and the long term safety and maintenance issues that may affect people or the performance of the building. (6%)

a. Thermal Insulation

i.   Common thermal insulation types, materials, applications, installation methods, and construction techniques
ii.   Typical defects (e.g., lack of insulation, uneven insulation, damaged insulation, flame spread concerns, improper clearances and alignment)
iii.   Theory of heat transfer and energy conservation
iv.   Performance parameters (e.g., R-value)
v.   Maintenance concerns and procedures
vi.   Safety issues, applicable standards, and appropriate terminology

b. Moisture Management

i.   Common vapor retarder types, materials, applications, installation methods, and construction techniques
ii.   Typical defects (e.g., inadequate ventilation, evidence of condensation)
iii.   Theory of moisture generation and movement

   iv. Performance parameters
   v. Vapor pressure and its effects
   vi. Theory of relative humidity
   vii. Effects of moisture on building components, occupants, and indoor air quality
   viii. Moisture control systems
   ix. Appearance or indications of excessive moisture and likely locations for condensation to occur
   x. Maintenance concerns and procedures
   xi. Safety issues, applicable standards, and appropriate terminology

c. Ventilation Systems of Attics, Crawl Spaces, and Roof Assemblies

   i. Common types, materials, applications, installation methods and construction techniques
   ii. Typical ventilation defects and how they affect buildings and people
   iii. Theory of air movement in building assemblies (e.g., conditioned vs. unconditioned)
   iv. Theory of relative humidity
   v. Interdependence of mechanical systems and ventilation systems
   vi. Appliance exhaust systems requirements (e.g., clothes dryers, range hoods, bathroom exhausts)
   vii. Screening, sizing, and location requirements for exhaust openings
   viii. Maintenance concerns and procedures
   ix. Safety issues, applicable standards, and appropriate terminology

Task 8 - The Plumbing System

Identify and inspect plumbing systems, using applicable standards for material selection and installation procedures, to assess immediate and long term safety and maintenance issues that may affect people or the performance of the building. (6%)

a. Water Supply Distribution System

   i. Common types, materials, applications, installation methods, and construction techniques
   ii. Typical modifications, repairs, upgrades, and retrofit methods and materials
   iii. Typical defects (e.g., cross-connection, backflow)
   iv. Common water pressure/functional flow problems and how they affect the water distribution system (e.g., water softeners, private well equipment, hard water build up, galvanized pipes, pressure reducer valves, expansion tanks)
   v. Pipe defect/deterioration issues (e.g., PVC, galvanized, brass, polybutylene, PEX)
   vi. Maintenance concerns and procedures
   vii. Safety issues, applicable standards, and appropriate terminology (e.g., understanding of term functional flow)

b. Fixtures and Faucets

   i. Common fixture and faucet types, materials, applications, installation methods, and construction techniques
   ii. Typical modifications, repairs, upgrades, and retrofit methods and materials
   iii. Typical defects (e.g., cross-connection/backflow, fixture attachment)
   iv. Maintenance concerns and procedures
   v. Safety issues, applicable standards, and appropriate terminology

c. Drain, Waste, and Vent Systems

    i.   Common types, materials, applications, installation methods, and construction techniques (e.g., supports/spacing)

    ii.   Typical modifications, repairs, upgrades, and retrofit methods and materials (e.g., connecting dissimilar piping materials)

   iii. Theory and usage of traps and vents

   iv. Identification of public or private disposal (when possible)

    v.   Typical defects (e.g., faulty installation, deterioration, leakage, defective venting or improper drain slope)

   vi. Maintenance concerns and procedures

  vii. Safety issues, applicable standards, and appropriate terminology (e.g., understanding of term functional drainage)

d. Water Heating Systems

    i.   Common types, materials, applications, installation methods, and construction techniques (e.g., storage, instant, tankless, indirectly heated, atmospheric/gravity/induced draft)

    ii.   Typical water heater defects (e.g., improper vent/flue materials and configuration, poor condition, unsafe locations, improper connections, compatible to fuel type, temperature and pressure relief system problems)

   iii. Accessory items (e.g., drain pans, seismic restraints, expansion tanks, recirculation systems)

   iv. Connections to and controls for energy source

    v.   Combustion air and makeup air air requirements

   vi. Maintenance concerns and procedures

  vii. Safety issues, applicable standards, and appropriate terminology

e. Fuel Storage and Fuel Distribution Systems

    i.   Common types, materials, applications, installation methods, and construction techniques

    ii.   Typical defects (e.g., piping supports/spacing, shutoff requirements, unprotected fuel lines, leaking fuel fittings)

   iii. Defects in above ground oil/gas storage tanks

   iv. Fuel leak indications, repairs, and remediation methods

    v.   Basic components of gas appliance valves and their functions

   vi. Tank restraints and supports

  vii. Underground storage tank indicators and reporting requirements

 viii. Maintenance concerns and procedures

f. Safety issues, applicable standards, appropriate terminology, drainage sumps, sump pumps, sewage ejector pumps, related valves and piping

    i.   Common types, materials, applications, installation methods, and construction techniques

    ii.   Typical defects (e.g., inoperative sump pumps, improperly installed/designed equipment and systems, alarms, lid seals)

   iii. Sump pump location significance

   iv. Pump discharge location significance

    v.   Maintenance concerns and procedures

   vi. Safety issues, applicable standards, and appropriate terminology

Task 9 - The House Interior

Identify and inspect house interior components, using applicable standards for material selection, installation procedures, and maintenance, to assess immediate and long term safety issues that may affect people or the performance of the building. (5%)

a. Walls, Ceiling, Floors, Doors, and Windows, and other Interior Components

i.   Types of defects in interior components not caused by defects in other systems (e.g., attachment defects, damage)

ii.   Typical defects in interior components caused by defects in other systems (e.g., structural movement, moisture stains)

iii.   Common wall, ceiling, floor, door, and window types, materials, applications, installation methods and construction techniques

iv.   Egress requirements (e.g., window security bar release, basement windows, opening size, sill height, and ladders)

v.   Applicable fire safety and occupancy separation requirements (e.g., fire separation, firewalls, fire separation doors, and penetrations of firewalls)

vi.   Operation of windows or doors

vii.   Fire and life safety equipment (e.g., smoke alarms and carbon monoxide alarms inoperative or missing)

viii.   Maintenance concerns and procedures

ix.   Safety issues, applicable standards, and appropriate terminology related to commonly encountered wall, ceiling, floor, door, and window types, materials, applications, installation methods, and construction techniques

b. Steps, Stairways, Landings, and Railings

i.   Common step, stairway, landing, and railing types, materials, applications, installation methods, and construction techniques

ii.   Maintenance concerns and procedures

iii.   Typical defects (e.g., loose/damaged components, improper rise/run, inadequate/omitted handrails)

iv.   Safety issues, applicable standards, and appropriate terminology

c. Garage Vehicle Doors and Operators

i.   Common garage vehicle doors and door operator types, materials, applications, installation methods, and construction techniques

ii.   Typical defects (e.g., damaged components, safety considerations, spring retention, door operator adjustment)

iii.   Maintenance concerns and procedures

iv.   Safety issues, applicable standards, and appropriate terminology

Task 10 - Fireplaces and Chimneys

Identify and inspect fireplace and chimney systems, using applicable standards for material selection and installation procedures, to assess immediate and long term safety and maintenance issues that may affect people or the performance of the building. (6%)

a. Fireplaces, Solid-Fuel-Burning Appliances, Chimneys, and Vents

   i.   Common manufactured fireplaces (e.g., vented, direct vent, unvented) and solid-fuel-burning appliance types, materials, applications, installation methods, and construction techniques
   ii. Common manufactured fireplaces and solid-fuel-burning appliance chimney, vent connector, and vent types, materials, applications, installation methods and construction techniques, including direct vent and unvented fireplaces
   iii. Common masonry fireplace and chimney types, materials, applications, installation methods, and construction techniques
   iv. Chimney terminations (e.g., spark arrestors, chimney cap)
   v.   Chimney foundation, height and clearance requirements
   vi. Theory of heat transfer
   vii. Effects of moisture and excessive heat on fireplaces and chimneys
   viii. Fuel types and combustion characteristics, air supply, and combustion air requirements
   ix. Typical defects (e.g., hearth defects, clearance requirements, firebox damage, damper problems, smoke chamber and flue issues, shared flue issues)
   x.   Operation of equipment, components, and accessories
   xi. Maintenance concerns and procedures
   xii. Safety issues, fire safety fundamentals, applicable standards, and appropriate terminology

Task 11 - Kitchen Appliances

Identify and inspect common permanently installed kitchen appliances for proper condition and operation. (3%)

a. Installation

b. Operating using normal controls

c. Typical defects (e.g., appliance not anchored/leveled, rusting racks, leaking unit, missing air gap)

d. Maintenance concerns and procedures

e. Safety issues, applicable standards, manufacturer's specifications, and appropriate terminology

Task 12 - Swimming Pools and Spas

Identify and inspect swimming pool and spa systems, using applicable standards for material selection and installation procedures, to assess immediate and long term safety and maintenance issues. (2%)

a. Types of construction

   i.   Perimeter coping and water level finish
   ii. Shell interior finish (e.g., plaster, vinyl, aggregate)
   iii. Entrapment prevention (e.g., dual drains, anti-entrapment covers)
   iv. Permanently installed handrails and ladders

b. Mechanical systems

    i.   Pump, motors, blowers, skimmer, filter, drains, gauges

    ii.   Pipes and valves

    iii.   Cleaning systems (e.g., in-floor cleaning systems, suction cleaning systems)

    iv.   Heating systems (e.g., gas, electric, solar)

c. Electrical systems

    i.   Lighting and GFCI protection

    ii.   Timers and controls

    iii.   External bonding (e.g., pump motors, blowers, heater cabinet)

d. Typical defects (e.g., inoperative equipment, pipe leaks, damage/deterioration of components)

e. Maintenance concerns and procedures

f. Safety issues (e.g., access barriers), applicable standards, and appropriate terminology

Task 13 - Landscape Irrigation Systems: Identify and inspect landscape irrigation systems, using applicable standards for material selection and installation procedures, to assess immediate and long term safety and maintenance issues that may affect the performance of the system and building. (1%)

a. Common material types, applications, installation methods, and construction techniques

    i.   Typical modifications, repairs, upgrades, and retrofit methods and materials

    ii.   Timers and controls (e.g., timing device, manual valves)

    iii.   Typical defects (e.g., leaks, poor adjustment, inoperative components, cross-connection/ backflow, proximity to and possible effects on building)

    iv.   Common water pressure/flow problems and how they affect the landscape irrigation system

    v.   Visible and accessible pipe deterioration issues (e.g., PVC, galvanized, brass)

    vi.   Maintenance concerns and procedures

    vii.   Safety issues,

PERFORMANCE DOMAIN II: ANALYSIS AND REPORTING OF FINDINGS (24%)

Task 1 - Minimum Report Contents

Identify building systems and components by their distinguishing characteristics (e.g., purpose, type, size, location) in the home inspection report to inform the client what was inspected. (5%)

a. Minimum information required in a home inspection report (e.g., property data, construction materials, installation techniques and procedures, locations of main system shutoffs)

b. Describing the type of systems and the location of system components

c. Correct technical terms to describe systems and components of the building

Task 2 - Inspection Methods and Limitations

Describe inspection methods and limitations in the home inspection report to inform the client what was inspected, what was not inspected, and the reason why it was not inspected. (6%)

a. Minimum and critical information required in a home inspection report (e.g., weather conditions, inspection safety limitations, components not accessible)

b. Common methods used to inspect particular components (e.g., roofs, attics, crawl spaces, mechanical components)

Task 3 - Deficiency Statements

Describe systems and components inspected that are not functioning properly or are defective. (7%)

a. Common expected service life of building and mechanical components

b. Common indicators of potential failure (e.g., rust and corrosion, unusual noise, excessive vibration, and/or lack of routine maintenance)

c. Common safety hazards

d. Common test instruments and their proper use for qualitative analysis (e.g., moisture meters, carbon monoxide meters, probes)

Task 4 - Action Recommendations

List recommendations to correct deficiencies or items needing further evaluation. (5%)

a. Correct professional or tradesperson required to perform repairs or to perform further evaluations

b. Common remedies for correction

c. Relationships between components in the building

d. When to immediately inform building occupants of a life threatening safety hazard (e.g., gas leak, carbon monoxide accumulation)

PERFORMANCE DOMAIN III: INSPECTION BUSINESS OPERATION (12%)

Task 1 - Contracts

Identify the elements of the written home inspection contract (e.g., scope, limitations, terms of services) to establish the rights and responsibilities of the home inspector and the client. (6%)

a. **Purpose of a contract**

b. **Elements of a contract (e.g., names of parties, scope of a home inspection, terms of service, exclusions and limitations, address, date and times of the home inspection, limits of liability, dispute resolution, and understanding state specific elements)**

c. **Timing of delivery and signing contract**

Task 2 - Legal Concepts and Insurance

Identify responsibilities to the client in order to maintain the quality, integrity, reputation, and objectivity of the home inspection process while protecting the interests of the client. (6%)

a. **Fundamental legal concepts (e.g., fiduciary responsibility, contractual responsibility, liability, negligence, due diligence, consumer fraud, knowledge of licensing requirements)**

b. **Identify conflicts of interest with reference to the client (e.g., home inspector interest in the property, third party stakeholders with financial interest in the outcome of the home inspection)**

c. **Boundaries of personal expertise and professional scope of practice (e.g., don't exceed your area of expertise)**

d. **Understand the types and purpose of financial protection (e.g., general liability insurance, professional errors and omissions insurance, bonding, and warranties)**

3: REFERENCE MATERIALS FOR THE NATIONAL HOME INSPECTOR EXAMINATION

Numerous actions are involved in maintaining the item bank (list of active questions) for use with the National Home Inspector Examination (NHIE). The performance of active questions as well as questions that have been recently written or edited are analyzed on a continual basis. Questions that have been analyzed and are performing well are added to the item bank throughout the year. Older questions are rotated out of the item bank as they are replaced by newer or more relevant questions within a topic area. The secondary reference materials listed below have been used as sources for a portion of the older questions on the examination. The secondary references are becoming less relevant to the NHIE as older questions are rotated out of the item bank. Eventually there will not be any questions on the NHIE that use these secondary reference materials as authoritative sources. For an up-to-date list of the reference materials for active questions on the NHIE please visit: http://www.homeinspectionexam.org/references.php

PRIMARY REFERENCES FOR NHIE QUESTIONS

ASHI @ HOME, Home Inspection Training Program Series
Carson, Dunlop & Associates, Ltd.

Code Check, A Guide to Building A Safe House, 7th Edition
Redwood Kardon and Douglas Hansen

Code Check Electrical, 7th Edition
Redwood Kardon and Douglas Hansen

Code Check Plumbing and Mechanical, 4th Edition
Redwood Kardon and Douglas Hansen

Everybody's Building Code 2012
Bruce A. Barker

International Residential Code 2012
International Code Council, Inc.

JLC Field Guide To Residential Construction, Volume 1
Hanley-Wood LLC

JLC Field Guide To Residential Construction, Volume 2
Hanley-Wood LLC

The Home Reference Book, 26th Edition
Carson Dunlop & Associates, Ltd.

The Home Reference Book Study Guide, 26th Edition
Carson Dunlop & Associates, Ltd.

SECODARY REFERENCES FOR NHIE QUESTIONS

APA Performance Rated I-Joists, 2001
The Engineered Wood Association

Engineered Wood Construction
The Engineered Wood Association, 2001

Essentials of Home Inspection Series
Carson Dunlops & Associates, Ltd.

Home Systems Illustrated, Third Edition
Tom Feiza, "Mr. Fix-It," Inc.

Means Illustrated Construction Dictionary, Third Edition
R.S. Means Company, Inc.

National Electrical Code 2011
National Fire Protection Association

Principles of Home Inspection Series
Carson Dunlop & Associates, Ltd.

The Illustrated Home, First Edition
Carson Dunlop & Associates, Ltd.

4: SCHEDULING AND TAKING THE NATIONAL HOME INSPECTOR EXAMINATION

A NOTE ABOUT BUILDING CODES

It is generally accepted that home inspectors are not expected to report code violations in inspected properties. The Role Delineation Study (RDS) on which the National Home Inspector Examination (NHIE) is based, however, reflects the actual practice of the profession as defined by surveys of home inspectors throughout the nation.

Furthermore, NHIE questions are written by home inspectors who are considered Subject Matter Experts (SMEs) These SMEs believe that knowledge of basic codes, especially regarding home safety, is vital to adequate practice of home inspection.

SUBJECT MATTER EXPERTS

SMEs are home inspectors who have different levels of experience in the field. These inspectors have between one and thirty years experience. This group includes those affiliated with professional associations, and those not who are not affiliated with professional associations. The group also includes code certified inspectors, and specialists in certain catagories.

EXAMINATION SCHEDULING PROCEDURES

The NHIE is administered by AMP, Pearson Vue, and PSI, depending on the state in which the NHIE is administered. Each testing company has an NHIE Candidate Handbook that is posted and available on their website. These handbooks contain all the testing company's policies and procedures for administering the NHIE. Candidates should thoroughly review the appropriate handbook.

Examination Fee

The examination fee is $225, but it may vary by state. The specific examination fee for a state is provided in the respective Candidate Handbook. The examination fee must be paid at the time of reservation by credit card or debit card. Payment will not be accepted at any test center.

Examination fees are not refundable or transferable. The examination fee will be forfeited if the test is not taken within one year of the date the examination fee is received. The fee is the same for each examination, whether the candidate is taking the examination for the first time or repeating the examination. The candidate may take the NHIE as many times as needed. The candidate must wait thirty days before taking the examination again.

Internet Registration

Candidates may schedule to take the NHIE by going to www.homeinspectionexam.org and clicking on the registration tab on the home page. The candidate will then be asked to select the state in which the examination will be taken. The candidate will then be linked to a secure website of the appropriate testing company. During this online registration process the candidate will select the location, date, and time to take the NHIE. The candidate will also be instructed to pay for the NHIE. The testing company will provide the candidate with an email confirmation. The candidate may schedule for the examination via the Internet twenty-four hours a day. If assisstance is needed during the registration process, call the testing companies:

AMP   800-345-6559

Pearson VUE   888-204-6230

PSI   800-733-9267

Telephone Registration

Telephone registrations can be made by calling the appropriate testing company. Candidates are encouraged to have the necessary information ready when making the call.

Candidates may call AMP at 800-345-6559 during the following hours to schedule an examination:

Monday – Thursday	7:00 am - 9:00 pm CST
Friday	7:00 am – 7:00 pm CST
Saturday	8:30 am - 5:00 pm CST

Candidates may call Pearson VUE at 888-204-6230 during the following hours to schedule an examination:

Monday – Friday	8:00 am – 11:00 pm EST
Saturday	8:00 am – 5:00 pm EST
Sunday	10:00 am – 4:00 pm EST

Candidates may call PSI at 800-733-9267, 24 hours a day to register using the Automated Registration System. The hours of operation for live operators are as follows:

Monday – Friday	7:30 am - 8:00 pm EST
Saturday	11:00 am – 5:00 pm EST

Fax Registration

AMP will accept registration by fax. Candidates must complete all sections of the Examination Registration Form and fax it to 913-895-4651. Within 24 hours of receiving the faxed registration form, AMP will fax the candidate a notice that it has been received. This option is available only for individuals paying the examination fee by credit card.

PSI will accept registration by fax. Candidates must complete all sections of the Examination Registration Form, including the candidates's credit card number and expiration date and fax it to 702-932-2666. Fax registrations are accepted 24 hours a day. If the candidate's information is incomplete or incorrect, it will be returned for correction. Please allow four business days to process the registration. After four business days, the candidate may call PSI to schedule the examination, 800-733-9267.

Mail Registration

AMP will accept standard mail registration. Candidates must complete all sections of the Examination Registration Form and mail it to AMP with the examination fee (paid by cashier's check or money order) to the address indicated on the form. This form will be returned if it is incomplete, illegible, or submitted with an incorrect fee. Call AMP at 800-345-6559 to schedule an examination appointment.

PSI will accept standard mail registration. Candidates must complete all sections of the Examination Registration Form and mail it to PSI with the examination fee (paid by cashier's check or money order) to the address indicated on the form. This form will be returned if it is incomplete, illegible, or submitted with an incorrect fee. The candidate should print his/her social security number on the check or money order to ensure that the fees are properly assigned. Please allow two weeks for processing of the registration before scheduling an examination appointment.

Cancelling and Rescheduling an Appointment

Candidates may reschedule the examination appointment with AMP once at no charge by calling AMP at 800-345-6559 at least two business days prior to the scheduled appointment. If the candidate fails to appear for the scheduled examination appointment, the following reasons may be considered: 1) hospitalization, 2) death in the immediate family, 3) disabling traffic accident, 4) court appearance or jury duty, or 5) military duty.

Candidates may cancel and reschedule an examination appointment with Pearson VUE at 888-204-6230 at least forty-eight hours before the examination. Candidates who change or cancel a reservation with proper notice may either transfer their fees to a new reservation or request a refund. Candidates who change or cancel their reservations without proper notice will forfeit the examination fee. Refunds for credit/debit cards are immediate, while refunds for electronic checks and vouchers will be processed in two to three weeks. Candidates are individually liable for the full amount of the examination fee once a reservation has been made, whether individually or by a third party.

Candidates may cancel and reschedule an examination appointment with PSI without forfeiting the fee if the cancellation notice is received two days before the scheduled examination date. The candidate may call PSI at 800-733-9267. Please note that the candidate may also use the automated system, using a touch-tone phone, twenty-four hours a day in order to cancel or reschedule the appointment. A voice mail message is not an acceptable form of cancellation. Please use the Internet, automated telephone system (IVR), or call PSI and speak to a Customer Service Representative.

Missed Appointment or Late Cancellation

A complete application and examination fee are required in order to reapply for the examination. For an examination through AMP, candidates will forfeit the application and all fees paid to take the examination under the following circumstances:

- The candidate wishes to reschedule an examination but fails to contact AMP at least two business days prior to the scheduled examination session.
- The candidate wishes to reschedule a second time.
- The candidate appears more than fifteen minutes late for an examination.
- The candidate fails to report for an examination appointment

For an examination through Pearson Vue, candidates who are late to or absent from an examination may be excused for the following reasons:
- Illness of the candidate or of the candidate's immediate family member
- Death in the immediate family
- Disabling traffic accident

- Court appearance or jury duty
- Military duty
- Weather emergency

Candidates who are late to an examination will not be admitted and will forfeit the examination fee. Candidates who are absent from an examination and have not changed or canceled the reservation according to the Change/Cancel Policy will forfeit the examination fee. Written verification and supporting documentation for requesting an excused absence must be submitted to Pearson VUE within fourteen days of the original examination date. Written verification and supporting documentation can be sent by fax or mailed to Pearson VUE.

For an exam through PSI, the candidate's registration will be invalid, the candidate will not be able to take the examination as scheduled, and the candidate will forfeit the examination fee if the candidate fails to:

- cancel the appointment two days before the scheduled examination date;
- appear for the examination appointment;
- arrive after the examination start time;
- present proper identification when you arrive for the examination.

Special Examination Arrangements

All examination centers are equipped to provide access in accordance with the Americans with Disabilities Act (ADA) of 1990, and every reasonable accommodation will be made in meeting the needs of a candidate. Applicants with disabilities or those who would otherwise have difficulty taking the examination should make a request for alternative arrangements with the respective testing company. Requests for any special accommodations should be made in writing, describing the specific accommodations that will be needed, and must include supporting documentation. Test accommodations are individualized and considered on a case by case basis.

Examination Site Closing for an Emergency

In the event that severe weather or other emergency forces the closure of an examination center on a scheduled examination date, the candidated will be contacted by the testing company. Every effort will be made to reschedule the examination at a convenient time as soon as possible.

Reporting to the Examination Site

On the day of the examination, candidates should arrive at least thirty minutes prior to the appointment, and check in with the examination center administrator. The candidate's identification and other documentation will be reviewed and he or she will be photographed for the Score Report. If the candidate arrives late, the candidate may not be admitted to the examination center and will forfeit the examination registration fee.

Required Identification at the Examination Site

Candidates who do not present the required items will be denied admission to the examination center, will be considered absent, and will forfeit the examination fee.

Candidates must provide two forms of identification. All identification must be in English. The name on the identification must exactly match the name on the registration form. One must be a VALID form of government issued identification (driver's license, state ID, passport, military ID), which bears the candidate's signature and photograph. The second ID must have the candidate's signature and preprinted legal name. A candidate with questions about acceptable forms of identification should contact the testing company.

Examination Site Security

Each testing company has its own security procedures which include, but are not limited to, video surveillance. There are strict limits on the personal belongings that a candidate may bring to an examination center, and there restrictions that candidates must abide by once at the center.

Orientation to the Examination Area

Candidates will be directed to a semiprivate testing station to take the examination. Before the candidate starts the examination, an introductory tutorial to the computer and keyboard is provided on the computer screen. Sample questions are included following the tutorial so that the candidate may practice using the keys, answering questions, and reviewing the answers.

The examination center administrators will answer questions regarding use of the computer, but candidates should be aware that the administrators are not familiar with the content of the examinations or with any state licensing requirements.

Candidates may begin the examination once they are familiar with the computer. The examination begins the moment a candidate looks at the first examination question.

Candidates will be given four hours (240 minutes) to complete the examination. The examination will end automatically after the examination time has expired, and candidates will leave the test center with their official scores in hand.

Pretest Questions

In addition to the number of questions per examination, up to twenty-five pretest questions may be administered to candidates during the examinations. These questions are included for question evaluation (vetting) purposes, but will not be scored, and the time taken to answer them will not count against examination time. The administration of such non-scored pretest questions is an essential step in developing future NHIE examinations.

Examination Review

Comments on questions on the NHIE are reviewed by the Examination Board of Professional Home Inspectors with the advice of its test development contractor. In no case will resolution of candidate comments result in the modification of individual candidate scores. Comments may affect future versions of the examination.

How the NHIE is Scored

The candidate's pass/fail status is determined by whether enough questions were answered correctly in order to meet or exceed the pass point of the examination. This pass point, or cut score, is established by a criterion-referenced methodology suggested in accepted standards for public protection examinations. This methodology is designed to ensure that home inspectors who pass the test are competent to practice in the public arena. The NHIE is scale scored from 200 to 800, with 500 as the pass point. It is important to keep in mind that the total score on the examination is not the average of the subscores in each of the content areas. Some content areas contain more questions than others. Also, the number of available points is not related to the number of questions, because items vary in difficulty, criticality, and importance to competent practice.

Reporting the Candidate's Score

The candidate's score will be given immediately following completion of the examination. The candidate will leave the test center with the official Score Report in hand. If the candidate receives a passing score, that document will be used with any regulatory agency or professional association as proof that the candidate has passed the NHIE. To become licensed, it is the responsibility of the candidate to follow through with the appropriate authority.

If the candidate does not pass, the candidate will receive a diagnostic report indicating strengths and weaknesses by examination type with the score report.

Using a Score Report

If the candidate took this examination to qualify for licensing or other regulation, contact the regulating agency in order to determine how to submit the passing score report. The candidate will find links to regulatory bodies at www.homeinspectionexam.org. If the candidate took this examination to qualify for a professional membership organization, contact that organization for instructions.

Duplicate Score Reports

Candidates may request a duplicate score report from the testing company.

Examination Center Policies

Each testing company has specific policies that must be followed at the individual examination centers. Their specific policies are detailed in their Candidate Handbook.

5: STRATEGIES FOR SUCCESS WHEN TAKING HIGH STAKES EXAMINATIONS

PURPOSE OF THIS CHAPTER

The purpose of this chapter is to provide candidates who have studied the reference material with advice on how to pass high stakes examinations. No test-taking strategies will help the candidate who is not prepared and does not know the material. On the other hand, knowledge of test-taking strategies can provide a higher degree of self confidence before and during the examination. In order to present a more generic view of these strategies, many of the examples shown include professions other than home inspection.

The following terms will be used throughout this chapter:

- **Item** – The examination question
- **Stem** – The part of the item that presents the question or problem
- **Options** – The choices offered
- **Key** – The correct choice
- **Distractors** – The incorrect choices

INTRODUCTION

Examinations are a fact of life, especially for people involved in regulated occupations. A license examination experience brings together two sets of professionals: the examination preparers and the candidates (those who take the examination).

Examination items are written by Subject Matter Experts (SMEs). These are people with knowledge of the trade who, under the supervision of testing professionals, write items that measure the knowledge needed to perform as a competent member of the profession. Well written items will deal with important aspects of trade practice. Poor items will deal with trivia. Items perceived by candidates as poor are usually the source of complaints claiming the item was tricky or no correct answer was provided.

HOW EXAMINATIONS ARE DEVELOPED

It is important to share some of the inside information on how examinations are developed. This will take away some of the mystery about how examination items are developed. Examination development is a science, and the items are carefully crafted. The candidate may not share that view when presented with what appears to be a trick question. High stakes examinations should follow certain guidelines or steps in their development, and this is governed by laws and professional standards.

The following is an overview of the process that should be followed in order to develop a high stakes examination.

1. A job analysis is conducted to find the most critical tasks that are required to perform the job. A typical job analysis might involve interviewing current job practitoners. They are asked to describe what they do on the job. Once the interviewers are convinced they have a comprehensive description of the tasks performed, they develop a questionnaire to be sent to a representative sample of job practitoners. Tasks are rated on dimensions such as amount of time spent on the task, importance of the task, and consequences of performing the task improperly. The results are analyzed in order to come up with the most critical tasks for the job. This refers to the previously mentioned Role Delineation Study (RDS). Critical tasks for a grocery store manager might include:

   - conduct price comparison surveys,

   - conduct sanitation inspections,

   - inspect department's shelf maintenance.

2. Once the critical tasks have been determined, it is important to find out what knowledge is required to perform the tasks. SMEs are asked to describe the knowledge areas and then link them to the critical tasks. The task: conduct sanitation inspections, might be linked to knowledge of food sanitation standards. A number of tasks may be linked to a particular knowledge area. In this way, weights are assigned to the most important knowledge areas. This becomes the basis of the examination blueprint.

3. An examination blueprint is created to determine how many items will be required for each of the knowledge areas. An examination blueprint for riggers is shown below:

Advanced Rigging Examination Plan

Knowledge Area	Number of Items
Wire Rope	6
Boom Assembly	10
Lift Planning	13
Advanced Rigging Practices	15
Personal Lifting	6
Total	50

4. SMEs are trained in item writing techniques and assigned knowledge areas for which they will write items. Below is a typical checklist used to guide item writers in their work.

Item Review Checklist

- What knowledge, skill or ability is this question testing?

- Is it an important enough concept to be included on the test, or is it trivial?

- Is it relevant to the profession, and does it reflect current practices?

- Is it at the entry level?

- Does it focus on one issue or problem?

- Is all necessary information given; is there any unnecessary information?

- Is it clearly written, unambiguous and straightforward with no tricks and no obscure terms or words?

- Is there only one correct answer?

- Are the distractors plausible/believable?

- Are there important differences between options?
- Does the item contain any biased or insensitive terms, or does it reflect negatively on destinations, vendors, organizations, or ethnic groups?
- Does the item contain clues for test-wise candidates?
- Where does it best fit in the content outline?
- What is the authoritative reference/source for this item?

5. SMEs review the items under the guidance of a testing professional. The review attempts to ensure the items are relevant, reflect current practice, and can be linked to a reference.

6. Those items that meet both content and process standards become items that may be added to an item bank.

7. Whenever possible, the new items are tested during actual examinations to determine if they perform as expected. An examination often will contain some items that will not be scored, but their performance will be monitored by testing professionals.

8. Items are subjected to statistical analysis and content analysis before being made part of the active items bank. In this process, a testing professional reviews statistics that will indicate if the item is discriminating well between qualified and unqualified candidates. If the statistics indicate a problem with the item, it will be reviewed again by SMEs to see what corrective measures can be taken with the content of the item. This is a point where candidate comment sheets can be very helpful. It seems that no matter how well an item has been reviewed, the real test of an item is when it is placed before actual candidates.

9. Using the examination blueprint, alternate forms of the examination are created. Because repeated use of a single examination form can let people become familiar with its contents, it is necessary to have alternative forms available. The alternative forms test the same material as the original, but with different questions. This is particularly important when failed candidates come back for a retest. If they see the same test, they may have an advantage.

10. A passing score is determined that will demonstrate minimal competence required for entry into the field. This is one of the most important areas in test development. This is the point when the examination developer asks the vital question: "What level of performance indicates that the candidate is qualified?"

11. The most widely accepted method of setting a passing score for occupational examinations is by use of criterion-referenced procedures. The heart of these methods is to determine what is called minimum competence. This is the minimal level of knowledge and skill required for licensure. The idea is to try to define this level and set a cut score that reflects it. These procedures are not trying to identify the super stars; rather, they are trying to identify people who can do the job properly and well. Under the guidance of a testing professional, a group of SMEs can develop the definition and use criterion referenced procedures to determine a passing score that best reflects this level of competence.

12. Examination development is never really finished. Performance of the items is regularly monitored to ensure that they are working correctly. After each examination administration, statistics are gathered to see if the examination as a whole is meeting certain standards regarding its performance. There are statistics that indicate if the examination is reliably measuring what it sets out to measure. In other words, can the examination be relied upon it to do its job the same way over and over again? In addition, there are statistics that indicate if the examination

items themselves are discriminating well. Using these performance statistics as guidelines, testing professionals can isolate items that are not doing the job. These items will be reviewed by SMEs to see if there are problems with how the item is constructed. If problems are found they will be corrected or the items will be deleted from the item bank. Examinations must be constantly monitored to see if they are performing as intended.

13. If a test is valid, it measures what it sets out to measure. The job analysis is vital to assuring that a plumbing test measures the knowledge and skills required to be a competent plumber. If a test is reliable it measures what it sets out to measure in a consistent manner. Assuming that the steps above have been followed, the test is valid and reliable, and the effect of measurement error is minimized.

TYPES OF ITEMS ON AN EXAMINATION

Most examinations will have three types of items. These are designed to measure different levels of competence. Expect to find a mixture of these types of items on the examination. Keep this in mind while studying the material in preparation for the examination. The following are examples of the three types.

<u>RECALL:</u> These items deal with memorized knowledge.

Which of the following beers is brewed in St Johns?

    A. La Batts

    B. Molson

    C. Moosehead

<u>APPLICATION:</u> These items use interpretation or classification of information; they often make use of formulas, graphics, or tables.

Which of the following is the best approach when trout fishing in the Canadian Rockies?

    A. Use a fly fishing system with a small insect lure

    B. Use a spinning system with a medium Mepps lure

    C. Use a bait casting system with a large night crawler

<u>ANALYSIS:</u> These items deal with problem solving and evaluating the best response to a situation presented.

Total parenteral nutrition (TPN) is initiated in a non-diabetic patient at a rate of 42 ml/hour. On the second day of therapy, serum and urine electrolytes are normal, urine glucose level is 3% and urine output exceeds parenteral intake. Which of the following is the MOST likely cause of these findings?

    A. The patient has developed an acute glucose tolerance.

    B. The patient's renal threshold for glucose has been exceeded.

    C. The patient is now Type 2 diabetic requiring supplemental insulin.

COMPUTER ADMINISTERED EXAMINATIONS

Computer administered examinations provide some advantages when taking the examination.

- One question at a time appears on the screen.

- Skipped questions are tracked.

- The candidate is warned about unanswered questions before being able to log out.

- Only one answer per question is accepted.

- No worry about failing to completely erase a changed answer.

- Time remaining is usually displayed on the screen.

CANDIDATE INFORMATION BULLETIN

One of the best sources of information to guide preparation for the examination is the Candidate Information Bulletin and the website of the test administrators. Some very important information is available including the following.

Examination site locations: the location of the various sites along with driving directions. Determine the best driving route to the site. Make a dry run to the site at the time of day you would be going on the test date. Find out what the parking situation is. Is parking free? Do not plan on feeding a meter during the examination.

Arrival time: how early should the candidate arrive? Be sure to allow plenty of extra time. Plan for unexpected delays. Depending on the efficiency of the administrators, checking in may take more time than expected. This might be viewed the same way we have come to look at air travel. Arriving early helps reduce stress.

Identification: acceptable forms of identification that you must have for admittance to the examination site. Check this carefully, some examination sites will require more than one form of identification. At least one photo identification will be required.

Security procedures: the types of items, such as cell phones, that are not permitted. In many places purses are not permitted in the examination room. Personal items may have to be put in transparent containers.

Computer based testing: an explanation of the procedures will be given along with an example of how the questions will look on the screen. The candidate will be given an opportunity to try a sample question on the computer before the actual examination begins.

Content Outline: provides information about how many questions will be on the examination, a list of the subject matter areas to be covered, the number of questions to expect for each content area, the length of time allowed for the examination, and the passing standard. Make use of this information when preparing for the test. By reviewing the outline for the examination, the candidate can determine which areas to emphasize during preparation for the examination.

References: provides a list references used to validate the information in the questions.

The foregoing information can be very useful because it provides a blueprint for what is allowed and not allowed into the examination room. The candidate and the administrator have a fixed, written set of rules that preclude arbitrary decisions.

ADMISSION LETTER

Another important document is the admission letter. This document, which will be sent after the online test application, contains important information including: the confirmation code, the name of the candidate, and the date and time to report. It will be mailed or emailed to the candidate. This letter is frequently lost or left behind. This letter, or the confirmation code, is required in order to take the examination.

REDUCING TEST ANXIETY

Most of us are familiar with the old real estate question: what are the three most important considerations in real estate? The answer is: location, location, location. Similarly, the three most important considerations in dealing with test anxiety are: preparation, preparation, preparation. Preparation means being prepared:

- with knowledge of the subject,

- with knowledge of what the test requires,

- by having all the appropriate materials in hand, and

- by being familiar with some tips and strategies for test taking.

Test anxiety can be significantly reduced by avoiding situations that can cause last minute panic.

- Make a dry run to the test site to find out how long it will take and what the parking situation is.

- Make a package of all the materials needed on the test day. This would include identification and the admission letter. Place these either in the car or by the door.

- Arrive at the test site early in order to survey the site and find the location of important facilities.

- Avoid individuals who appear to be overly stressed. Anxiety can be contagious.

- It is ok to skip questions and come back to them later.

- Skip the math questions and save them for later. They are time burners.

- Get a good night's sleep on the night before the examination.

Try to maintain a positive attitude while preparing for and during the examination. Don't get angry at the faceless authorities that require the examination. This only diverts energy from the task at hand.

The candidate is advised to focus on his/her own examination. If others finish sooner, it could be that they are taking a completely different examination, they may really know the material, or they may have just given up. Concentrate on your own performance.

Examination Time

The candidate should organize his/her materials upon arrival at his/her seat. Place any personal items in the appropriate area. The candidate should determine if the keyboard and the mouse are needed. Sometimes everything can be done with the mouse, and the keyboard can be moved aside to allow for more work space.

Read the examination instructions and ask questions of the proctor if there is anything that is unclear.

The computer will allow the candidate to mark items about which he/she is uncertain, and the candidate can return to them later. The computer will usually alert candidates who try to end the examination with unanswered items.

Read each stem (the part of the question that presents the question or problem) carefully. Try to formulate an answer before reading the options.

Item Strategies

The distractors: all of the above, and none of the above, are not allowed. As a result, examination writers often choose the exception model, as in: All of the following procedures are proper EXCEPT. The problem here is that this form makes the candidate shift mental gears. Instead of looking for a single correct answer, the candidate is looking for a single <u>wrong</u> answer. The item is asking the candidate to identify the action or procedure that is <u>not</u> correct. This can penalize fast readers. In the rush to finish the examination, a candidate accepts the first right answer seen, and thereby answers the item incorrectly. In these cases, view the item as a series of true or false statements. Is option A a proper procedure? If true, then it is <u>not</u> the correct answer. The true or false test should be applied until the candidate finds the one procedure or action that is <u>not</u> correct. The answer that is <u>not</u> correct is the exception, which is what the question is asking. That is the correct answer. Exception items are places where candidates should to slow down and read very carefully.

The candidate should read the item and highlight the key word in the item. The key word, when reading the item for the second time, may change the entire item from what it appeared to be upon the first reading. Beware of words such as: always, never, must, except, minimum, maximum, older, and newer.

Best Answer

Another area is the matter of the <u>best</u> answer. In some examinations, situations arise which may penalize the ablest or most experienced candidate. If the candidate has been in the profession for a long time the candidate may have seen it all. A common error made by candidates is to look at all the options and decide that none of them are absolutely correct. That, of course, is real life. Here, however, is a situation where the candidate should slow down and read carefully; thinking: what is the best answer of the group offered? The candidate may not completely agree with the option, but there are only four choices and the candidate must pick one. If a candidate believes that the item is flawed, the item should be cited when filling out the comment sheets provided by the administrator.

Qualifiers

The candidate should be particularly mindful of item stems that include qualifiers such as: most, least, maximum, minimum, greatest, and least. Items using these qualifiers set up a situation where a threshold number is being sought. Even if some of the other choices are right, they do not meet the referenced answer.

Low-voltage holiday detectors may be used when working with nonconductive coatings no GREATER than:

    A. 10.0 mils in thickness

    B. 20.0 mils in thickness

    C. 30.0 mils in thickness

    D. 40.0 mils in thickness

While choice A is correct, only choice B meets the requirement of the rule.

In some cases, the choices may be given in ranges:

    Less than 50 but not more than 100,

    More than 100 but less than 200.

This is done so that a candidate cannot reverse engineer the answer by plugging in the numbers and working through them.

Strategic Guessing

Another useful strategy is strategic guessing. In any four-part multiple choice question, the candidate has a 25% probability of guessing the correct answer. Sometimes that probability can be improved. If the candidate determines that two of the choices are clearly wrong, the probability of guessing correctly improves to 50%. The choice becomes one of two rather than one of four. Strategic guessing does not mean selecting one answer, such as A, for all guesses. Strategic guessing does mean answering every question with the best guess. The question left unanswered is always wrong.

Be alert for grammatical inconsistencies between the item stem and the options provided. A choice is almost always wrong if it and the stem do not make a grammatically correct sentence.

An effective method for reducing conflict is to:

    A. helping stop co-workers arguments.

    B. admit a problem exists.

    C. not discussing the things that upset you

    D. reacting to anything that upsets you

Clearly B is the only choice that is grammatically, as well as factually, correct.

What to do When Unsure

If one choice has significantly more information than the other choices, there is a strong chance it is the correct one.

When performing spray coating applications, the sprayer should be kept:

  A. 10 to 12 inches from the surface.

  B. At a 90 degree angle to, and 6 to 8 inches from, the surface.

  C. 14 to 20 inches from the surface.

  D. 3 to 5 inches from the surface.

Choice B gives more precise information about how the sprayer should be employed and is most likely to be the correct answer.

If a term is found in the stem of the question and appears in only one of the choices it is probably the answer.

What group was known as the Magnificent Seven?

  A. a touring softball team

  B. a group of seven cowboys

  C. a rock and roll group

  D. a football defensive line

In this case Seven and seven should add up.

At The End

Check the computer to ensure that all items have been properly marked.

This is the last chance to change an answer, but use this opportunity with caution. The first guess is most likely to be correct. Be sure to have a sound reason for changing the answer. Many candidates have changed themselves out of a passing score.

Make sure that to answer every question. An unmarked answer is always wrong. In a four-part multiple choice examination there is a one in four chance of getting the right answer. It is better to guess than to leave a question unanswered.

The Question/Comment Form

Examination administrators provide question or comment forms for the candidates. This is an important opportunity to ask questions about some of the items. Was there no correct answer, or more than one correct answer? Was there a failure to provide all the necessary information to properly answer the question? These forms are closely reviewed by the authors of the examinations. Questions can be very helpful in improving the quality of the examination. These questions can also be instrumental in having a question thrown out or changing the question and its answers.

Challenging Items on the Examination

As hard as examination authors try, there are times when the examination has items that are clearly incorrect. If a candidate believes that this is the situation, there is usually a formal process by which the items on the examination may be challenged. The procedures differ among jurisdictions, but are usually spelled out by the examination provider. The process may entail a review of the examination with a member of the testing authority. If a candidate is ready to make such a challenge, be sure to have carefully reviewed the reference that supports the challenge. Any challenge of this kind must have clear supportable evidence. It is kind of like getting a call on the field overturned by review; you must have clear and convincing evidence.

Summary

If there is a theme in the forgoing, it is that a candidate can demonstrate competence in the profession by studying the material, taking steps to ensure that there are few, if any surprises in the examination situation, and taking advantage of test taking tips and strategies. A properly developed licensing examination will be written by experienced job practitioners under the guidance of examination specialists. Both groups are interested in creating an examination that accurately measures what a competent professional needs to know.

6: SAMPLE EXAMINATION QUESTIONS

1. Buckling in horizontal vinyl siding is generally caused by

    A. reflected sunlight.
    B. improper fastening.
    C. condensation in walls.
    D. improper house wrap.

2. At what level would water pressure within a single-family dwelling begin to be considered excessive and require correction?

    A. 60 psi
    B. 80 psi
    C. 100 psi
    D. 120 psi

3. A newer home with electric heat is being inspected. It has a below grade finished basement containing a bedroom. The inspector should look for a smoke alarm and

    A. an escape and rescue opening.
    B. a carbon monoxide alarm.
    C. a fire extinguisher.
    D. a safety ladder.

4. A swimming pool fence must prevent passage of a sphere that is larger than

    A. 2 inches.
    B. 3 inches.
    C. 4 inches.
    D. 5 inches.

5. Refer to the photograph to answer this question. What should an inspector recommend to the client regarding the conditions shown in relation to the downspout/rain leader?

    A. Nothing, the downspout is properly installed.
    B. Gravel should be installed under the downspout.
    C. The downspout should be moved away from the siding.
    D. A contractor should evaluate the downspout and recommend repairs.

6. If water infiltration is suspected behind a finished surface. What tool would be the best choice to verify dampness?

    A. an infrared thermometer
    B. a pin-type moisture meter
    C. a non-contact moisture meter
    D. a digital camera

7. Gas-fired furnace heat exchangers most often fail from

    A. low temperatures.
    B. lack of use.
    C. improper gas pressure.
    D. rust and metal fatigue.

8. Relative Humidity (RH) is expressed as

    A. volume.
    B. percentage.
    C. capacity.
    D. temperature.

9. Connections of dissimilar metal in a plumbing system, such as galvanized steel pipe and copper pipe, will usually cause

    A. reduced water pressure.
    B. decreased water quality.
    C. glazed pipes.
    D. electrolysis.

10. A Ground fault circuit interrupter (GFCI) is a safety device that

    A. disconnects power when the grounding to the outlet is faulty.
    B. detects moisture and disconnects power in wet locations.
    C. disconnects the power when sensing current leakage to ground.
    D. protects against electrical surges and voltage spikes.

11. An electrical system with a fuse on the neutral conductor and on the energized (hot) conductors

    A. is twice as safe as a system where only the energized (hot) conductors are fused.
    B. should have the neutral conductor fuse sized to one half the normal ampacity for the circuit.
    C. is overfused up to 50% if used only for lighting.
    D. is hazardous and should be corrected.

12. To operate a central air conditioner, an electric clothes dryer, and an electric range, the ampacity of the service to the house should be AT LEAST

    A. 100 amps at 120 volts.
    B. 125 amps at 120 volts.
    C. 60 amps at 240 volts.
    D. 100 amps at 240 volts.

13. A floor joist in a crawl space has been cut where the toilet drain passes through the floor. The joists are 2x6 spaced at 16" on center. The inspector should recommend that

    A. the buyer monitor the floor. Floor systems such as this have redundant framing and removal of one joist is insignificant.
    B. a contractor should support the cut joist with new piers and posts from below.
    C. the cut joist should be headed off to adjacent framing members to distribute the load.
    D. a contrator be contacted to determine what is needed and make repairs.

14. Most problems with concrete are caused at the time of installation. What single factor causes the MOST problems?

    A. The concrete has insufficient thickness.
    B. Too much water is added to the mix.
    C. Too much Portland cement is in the mix.
    D. The wrong kind of sand is in the mix.

15. Brick chimneys on older properties with oil heat sometimes curve above the roof line, with no visible cracks. Which is a possible cause of this curving?

    A. settlement of the chimney footing
    B. expansion of mortar
    C. absence of a cricket flashing at the roof
    D. lack of a rain cap on the flue

16. Which set of building terms do NOT belong together?

    A. cripple trimmer, purlin
    B. arch, header, lintel
    C. rafters, ceiling joists, trusses
    D. sheathing, flooring, decking

17. Which has the LEAST effect on the deflection of a dimension lumber floor system?

    A. joist width
    B. joist grade
    C. joist species
    D. joist spacing

18. The normal MAXIMUM rise of residential stair treads is

    A. 5 ¼ inches.
    B. 7 ¾ inches.
    C. 8 ½ inches.
    D. 9 ¾ inches.

19. An ungrounded receptacle may be replaced by a ground fault circuit interrupter installed

    A. on the same phase as the receptacle.
    B. upstream from the receptacle.
    D. downstream from the receptacle.
    C. anywhere in the receptacle branch circuit.

20. Circuit breakers

    A. protect inhabitants by limiting shock duration.
    B. regulate power to the attached equipment.
    C. protect the wire from an electrical overload.
    D. measure the current in a circuit.

21. In a forced air heating system containing a split system air conditioner and a humidifier, humidity is reduced by

    A. running the humidifier in reverse.
    B. condensation at the condenser coil.
    C. condensation at the evaporator coil.
    D. condensation within the compressor.

22. A home inspection report MUST include

    A. the general life expectancy of the roofing material.
    B. information on flammability of the roof material.
    C. the type of roof material and the method of observation.
    D. the age of the roof.

23. Water hammer can occur as a result of

    A. a lack of air chambers.
    B. faulty shutoff valves.
    C. loose piping.
    C. low static water pressure.

24. If a system designed for use with natural gas is supplied with propane gas

    A. no changes are needed for the equipment to function properly.
    B. the flame will be too high unless a smaller orifice is installed.
    C. the flame will be too low unless a larger orifice is installed.
    D. the gas regulator and valve must be replaced.

25. Low pressure boiler pipes do NOT carry steam pressure above

    A. 15 psi.
    B. 12 psi.
    C. 9 psi.
    D. 6 psi.

26 When an asphalt shingle roof is installed over existing shingles, leakage commonly occurs at the

    A. eaves.
    B. penetrations.
    C. ridge.
    D. hips.

27. Roof trusses

    A. may be cut or modified in the field.
    B. make drywall nail pops less likely.
    C. cannot be used for long ceiling spans.
    D. are usually designed for two-point bearing.

28. On a hillside house with foundation drain systems,

    A. rock-filled foundation drains are not allowed on the interior side of the foundation.
    B. the roof drains should connect directly to the foundation drains and have cleanouts.
    C. all foundation drain systems must be in perforated plastic piping extending to daylight.
    D. the foundation drain systems collect water passing laterally through the slope.

29. A subpanel in an older house that is wired with non-metallic sheathed cable (NM) has one circuit with a ground wire. The ground wire

    A. should be connected to a separate grounded buss bar.
    B. should be connected to a separate ground rod.
    C. may be bonded using the panel cover screws.
    D. may be connected to the neutral buss bar.

30. Inspecting a very old country house, a gurgling sound is heard from the tub drain when the toilet is flushed. Which of the following is the MOST likely explanation for the sound?

    A. Water discharging from the toilet is pulling water from the tub trap.
    B. The tub drain is partially blocked.
    C. Water discharging from the toilet is pushing air through the tub trap.
    D. The branch drain is partially blocked downstream from the tub.

31. You are inspecting an older home which has replacement windows and new vinyl siding. The new siding is backed up with rigid foam insulation that covers the service entrance cable from the weatherhead to the meter. You should report that this is

    A. acceptable because the siding is a non-conducting type.
    B. an improper installation that should be corrected.
    C. a benefit because additional protection is provided to the service entrance cable.
    D. acceptable, provided the drip loops at the service entrance head are left exposed.

32. When looking at the exterior wall of a sixty year old brick masonry house with a gable roof, you notice a horizontal crack in the mortar and outward brick displacement along the gutter edge of the roof. The displacement is greatest at the center of the top three courses of brick. This condition is MOST likely caused by

    A. excessive sand in the mortar mix.
    B. defective brick bonding.
    C. improper ceiling joist installation.
    D. differential settlement.

33. You inspect a wood framed cantilevered balcony off a second-story bedroom. You find significant wood deterioration (at least one-half member depth) of all cantilever joists at the bearing point of the house. You should

    A. notify the occupants of the significant hazard, advise immediate repair to both the occupant and client in the report.
    B. note the significant hazard and recommend immediate repair, by licensed professional, in your report.
    C. refer the wood deterioration to a structural pest control operator for professional opinion.
    D. recommend sistering existing framing members to increase strength, prior to further use.

34. When a cooling unit is located in an attic where damage may result from condensate overflow

    A. attic ventilation must be increased to avoid condensation.
    B. steel ducting is not allowed because of potential damage from condensation.
    C. an auxillary condensate drain system is required.
    D. a supplemental condensate pump is required.

35. Asphalt shingles are NOT allowed to be installed on roofs with slopes less than

    A. 1 in 12.
    B. 2 in 12.
    C. 3 in 12.
    D. 4 in 12.

36. If a poured concrete foundation has an unusually large number of vertical cracks, each no wider than 1/32 inch, the cause is likely to be

    A. differential settlement from adverse drainage conditions.
    B. excessive amounts of aggregate in the concrete mix.
    C. settlement from compaction of soils below the footings.
    D. shrinkage of the concrete from excess water at the time of pouring.

37. Where should squash blocks (web blocking) be found in a wood I-joist floor system?

    A. at bearing ends and load bearing walls above with support girders below
    B. at bearing ends and all splices
    C. at bearing ends and plumbing penetrations
    D. at perimeter ends, plumbing penetrations, and splices over girders

38. Columns typically support

    A. footers.
    B. walls.
    C. girders.
    D. joists.

39. Oriented strand board (OSB) is used MOST frequently in

    A. roof, floor, and exterior wall sheathing.
    B. walls and interior sheathing.
    C. ceramic tile underlayment.
    D. vinyl tile underlayment.

40. Which of the following is NOT a component of wood stairs?

    A. riser
    B. header
    C. stringer
    D. tread

41. When inspecting the structural system, the inspector is required to

    A. inspect only the visible components in the attic and crawl space.
    B. specify method of structural repairs to the system.
    C. report all structural deficiencies observed.
    D. determine the cause and origin of the damage.

42. A ground fault occurs when

    A. too many devices are used on a circuit.
    B. a hot conductor touches another hot conductor.
    C. a hot conductor touches a grounded surface or grounding conductor.
    D. a grounded conductor comes in contact with a grounding conductor.

43 Electrical receptacles in bathrooms should be

    A. GFCI protected.
    B. at least 3 feet away from showers and bathtubs.
    C. not more than 2 feet from the vanity basin.
    D. waterproofed.

44. Medium efficiency furnaces have a draft inducer fan and are connected directly to the vent system instead of having a draft hood. There are white and yellowish deposits below the draft inducer fan. A possible explanation for these deposits is that

    A. the seal between the draft inducer fan and the furnace is failing.
    B. moisture is condensing in the vent and running back into the draft inducer fan.
    C. the draft inducer fan is not operating properly.
    D. the furnace has failed and is unsafe to operate.

45. The purpose of a trap in the waste drainage system is to

    A. provide maintenance access.
    B. prevent siphoning.
    C. block sewer gases.
    D. cause water to drain smoothly.

46. A home inspection typically includes an examination of

    A. adequacy of heat supply.
    B. heat exchangers.
    C. humidifiers.
    D. vents, flues, and chimneys.

47. In new construction, the MINIMUM overhead electrical service clearances are

    A. walkway: 8 feet, roadway: 16 feet, deck: 10 feet
    B. walkway: 9 feet, roadway: 15 feet, deck: 12 feet
    C. walkway: 10 feet, roadway: 18 feet, deck: 10 feet
    D. walkway: 12 feet, roadway: 20 feet, deck: 12 feet

48. During a summertime inspection, what could indicate chronic condensation problems in an attic?

    A. The attic is very warm.
    B. There is no vapor retarder on the insulation.
    C. There are gray/black stains on the north side roof sheathing.
    D. There are mildew stains on the bathroom ceilings.

49. Ice damming at the eaves may be caused by

    A. inadequate attic insulation.
    B. undersized gutters.
    C. shallow roof slope.
    D. improper flashing.

50. The purpose of flashing on a roof is to

    A. shed water onto roofing materials.
    B. seal roof shingles to vertical surfaces.
    C. protect roofing material.
    D. join different roofing materials.

51. The house you are inspecting currently has a gas-fired furnace or boiler. Each of the following clues may indicate that the house also has an abandoned buried fuel oil storage tank EXCEPT

    A. small diameter copper tubes emerging from the inside of the foundation wall or the floor near the furnace or boiler
    B. an approximately 1 ¼ inch diameter vent pipe outside coming from underground up against the foundation
    C. the brick chimney serving the furnace or boiler has deteriorated mortar joints at the bottom
    D. your knowledge that the neighborhood had or still has some houses served by oil heat

52. While inspecting a heat pump in the cooling mode, you measure a 28 degrees F temperature differential between the interior supply and return air. You should suspect

    A. an exterior fan running too slowly.
    B. an overheating compressor.
    C. a dirty filter.
    D. a thermostat set too low.

53. What is the MINIMUM electrical service drop clearance from a residential driveway?

    A. 12 feet
    B. 13 feet
    C. 15 feet
    D. 18 feet

54. The reason a dielectric union would be used in plumbing distribution pipes is to

    A. ensure that the grounding conductor has a secure connection.
    B. separate two dissimilar metals to prevent corrosion.
    C. isolate any electrical wires touching the supply pipes.
    D. bond the hot and cold water pipes.

55. A basin makes a gurgling sound at the end of draining the fixture. This may be due to

    A. improperly supported pipes.
    B. inadequate venting.
    C. an undersized drain pipe.
    D. improper drain slope.

56. Condensation between glass layers of thermal pane windows indicates the need to

    A. repair or replace sealant.
    B. repair or clean breather holes.
    C. replace glazing, sash, or window.
    D. replace the interior pane.

57. Dielectric unions

    A. accommodate pipe expansion.
    B. are undesirable and indicate a problem.
    C. prevent galvanic action.
    D. help maintain electrical grounding of pipes.

58. The MINIMUM clearance between a wood stove single wall vent connector and combustible materials should be

    A. 3 inches.
    B. 9 inches.
    C. 18 inches.
    D. 36 inches.

59. Garage door opener electronic eye sensors are properly installed when facing each other

    A. 1 to 3 inches above the garage floor.
    B. 4 to 6 inches above the garage floor.
    C. 7 to 10 inches above the garage floor.
    D. 11 to 15 inches above the garage floor.

60. Capillary tubes are part of the

    A. evaporator coil.
    B. heat exchanger.
    C. condenser coil.
    D. compressor discharge.

61. As a lintel over doors and windows in a masonry wall rusts it may cause

    A. the window glass to crack.
    B. the wall at the top to push out.
    C. cracks at the tops of openings.
    D. the lintel to rotate and displace the brick.

62. Roof truss uplift can cause cracks to form

    A. above exterior doors and windows.
    B. at interior wall/ceiling intersections.
    C. in bottom chords of roof trusses.
    D. in top chords of roof trusses.

63. When measuring the temperature drop across the evaporator in a central air conditioning system, a properly running unit on a humid summer day should read between

    A. 5° F and 15° F
    B. 15° F and 25° F
    C. 25° F and 35° F
    D. 35° F and 45° F

64. Knob and tube wiring may be acceptable if

    A. the home is insulated with fiberglass.
    B. the circuit breaker system is proper.
    C. not covered by insulation.
    D. the fuse system is still in place.

65. The MAXIMUM acceptable variation in riser heights within a flight of stairs is

    A. ½ inch.
    B. ⅜ inch.
    C. ¾ inch.
    D. 1 inch.

66. While conducting an inspection, your ladder falls over and breaks the homeowner's priceless Ming vase. What type of insurance is needed to cover the replacement?

    A. general liability
    B. homeowner's
    C. errors and omissions
    D. bonding

67. What is the MINIMUM allowable separation between a masonry chimney and combustible materials?

    A. 3/4 inch
    B. 1 inch
    C. 2 inches
    D. 4 inches

68. Bonding of appliances can be confirmed by using a/an

    A. volt meter.
    B. receptacle tester.
    C. ohm meter.
    D. ammeter.

69. The service panel enclosure door is required to open at least

    A. 45°.
    B. 90°.
    C. 135°.
    D. 180°.

70. Which of the following is a common maintenance task for a residential refrigeration system?

    A. clean the heat exchanger
    B. replace refrigerant
    C. clean the condenser coil
    D. replace the thermostat

71. The device used to detect the electrical current to the electric heater coil is called

    A. an anemometer.
    B. an ohm meter.
    C. a volt meter.
    D. an ammeter.

72. The inspector is required to operate all of the following EXCEPT

    A. shutoff valves.
    B. manual garage door.
    C. a representative number of windows.
    D. folding attic stairs.

73. Potable water systems connected to lawn irrigation systems need to be protected from

    A. backsiphonage.
    B. excess water usage.
    C. mechanical damage.
    D. low water flow.

74. Most modern kitchen ranges are required to have

    A. front edge controls.
    B. a warming drawer.
    C. an anti-tip device.
    D. a tipping alarm.

75. The inclusion of photographs in home inspection reports is

    A. optional.
    B. mandatory.
    C. discriminatory.
    D. illegal.

76. A home inspector should probe

    A. where decay is suspected.
    B. spalling in concrete.
    C. a representative number of floor joists.
    D. around a toilet.

77. Overhead electrical service should be a MINIMUM of how many feet above a flat roof subject to foot traffic?

    A. 4 feet
    B. 6 feet
    C. 8 feet
    D. 10 feet

78. One of the purposes of a home inspection contract is to define the responsibilities and limitations for

    A. the real estate agent.
    B. the client.
    C. the seller.
    D. the appraiser.

79. What is a required element of a contract?

    A. consideration
    B. real estate agent's name
    C. seller's name
    D. names of persons attending the inspection

80. Home inspection agreements (contracts) should

    A. establish the limitations of the inspection.
    B. be as exculpatory as possible.
    C. describe the weather conditions allowed.
    D. include the name of the client's real estate agent.

81. Stringer, tread, and riser are all components of a

    A. truss system.
    B. floor system.
    C. stair system.
    D. wall system.

82. The final decision to enter a crawl space is made

    A. when the home inspection is booked.
    B. by the homeowner.
    C. by the home inspector.
    D. by the client and agent.

83. The purpose of a contract is to protect the

    A. homeowner.
    B. real estate agent.
    C. buyer/client.
    D. home inspector and client.

84. Conducting a complete and thorough home inspection minimizes the need for

    A. a contract.
    B. errors and omissions insurance.
    C. bonding.
    D. a detailed inspection report.

85. What is the most common contributing factor to masonry retaining wall movement?

    A. corbelled construction
    B. hydrostatic pressure
    C. poorly mortared joints
    D. too many tiebacks

86. How are the holes in rigid foundation drain pipe aligned?

    A. toward the foundation
    B. on the top half of the pipe
    C. on the bottom half of the pipe
    D. away from the foundation

87. What is the primary purpose of control joints placed in concrete driveways?

    A. to prevent cracks
    B. to drain the surface
    C. to reduce random cracking
    D. to enhance appearance

88. Where might you expect to find a window with safety glass?

    A. less than 18 inches above the floor
    B. less than 24 inches above the floor
    C. above a kitchen sink
    D. on the second story

89. What is a common cause of buckled hardwood flooring in an existing house?

    A. excessive moisture
    B. lack of moisture
    C. improper installation
    D. poor quality material

90. A newly built ventilated crawl space with a vapor retarder is REQUIRED to have one square foot of net ventilation opening per

    A. 150 square feet of crawl space.
    B. 600 square feet of crawl space.
    C. 1,200 square feet of crawl space.
    D. 1,500 square feet of crawl space.

91. A standard claims made errors and omissions insurance policy includes claims filed

    A. during the time the policy is in effect.
    B. after the policy has lapsed.
    C. before the policy effective date.
    D. while the inspector maintains any required license.

92. Refer to the photograph to answer this question. What common defect is visible in the photograph of the entry steps?

    A. The riser height is too high.
    B. The hand rail is missing.
    C. The tread depth is too shallow.
    D. The tread depth is uneven.

93. Refer to the photograph to answer this question. What component is the arrow pointing to in the picture of the roof framing?

    A. rafter
    B. ridge board
    C. purlin
    D. strongback

94. Refer to the photograph to answer this question. Some inspectors measure the electricity used by a condenser. The numerals on the readout show

    A. ohms.
    B. amps.
    C. volts.
    D. watts.

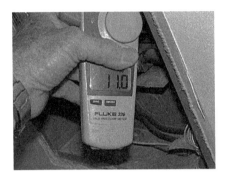

95. Refer to the photograph to answer this question. The truss roof framing in the photograph is

    A. proper and normal.
    B. field altered.
    C. in need of cripples.
    D. in need of a purlin.

96. Refer to the photograph to answer this question. The testing of garage doors with a wood block

    A. damages the door panels.
    B. irritates the opener mechanism.
    C. is improper.
    D. is the approved testing method.

97. Refer to the photograph to answer this question. The device shown in the photo is a

    A. backflow preventer.
    B. pressure reducer valve.
    C. gas pressure regulator.
    D. backwater valve.

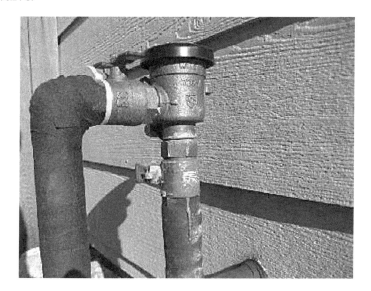

98. Refer to the photograph to answer this question. The photograph shows a dryer exhaust termination near a gas-fired water heater vent termination. The home inspector should recommend that

    A. the dryer exhaust termination should be at least 5 feet from gas vent termination.
    B. the dryer exhaust backdraft damper should be repaired or replaced to prevent entry of combustion gasses.
    C. the gas vent is improperly terminated and should be relocated.
    D. the client monitor the gas vent for indications of deterioration caused by the moist air from the dryer exhaust.

99. Refer to the photograph to answer this question. The heating system in the photograph is a

    A. forced air furnace.
    B. gravity flow steam boiler.
    C. pump circulating hot water boiler.
    D. gravity flow warm air furnace.

100. Please refer to the figure to answer this question. The figure shows a roof and chimney. The water is diverted around the chimney by the

    A. bird's mouth.
    B. cricket.
    C. swale.
    D. camelback.

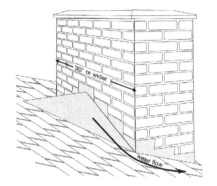

ANSWERS TO SAMPLE EXAMINATION QUESTIONS

1. B	26. B	51. C	76. A
2. B	27. D	52. C	77. D
3. A	28. D	53. A	78. B
4. C	29. A	54. B	79. A
5. D	30. A	55. B	80. A
6. C	31. B	56. C	81. C
7. D	32. C	57. C	82. C
8. B	33. A	58. C	83. D
9. D	34. C	59. B	84. B
10. C	35. B	60. A	85. B
11. D	36. D	61. C	86. C
12. D	37. A	62. B	87. C
13. D	38. C	63. B	88. A
14. B	39. A	64. C	89. A
15 B	40. B	65. B	90. D
16. A	41. C	66. A	91. A
17. A	42. C	67. C	92. A
18. B	43. A	68. C	93. C
19. B	44. B	69. B	94. B
20. C	45. C	70. C	95. B
21. C	46. D	71. D	96. D
22. C	47. C	72. A	97. A
23. A	48. C	73. A	98. C
24. B	49. A	74. C	99. D
25. A	50. A	75. A	100. B

7: INDEX